THE FOOD HYGIENE HANDBOOK

Richard A. Sprenger
B.Sc. (Hons.), D.M.S., F.C.I.E.H., F.S.O.F.H.T., M.R.E.H.I.S.

Director of Environmental Services
Doncaster Metropolitan Borough Council

Illustrations by
Graham Whitehouse

First Published 1982
Republished 1985/86/87/89/91/92/93
Ninth Edition October 1995
Reprinted April 1996

© HIGHFIELD PUBLICATIONS

"Vue Pointe", Spinney Hill, Sprotbrough,
Doncaster DN5 7LY, U.K.
Tel: Doncaster (01302) 850007
Facsimile: (01302) 311112

ISBN 1 871912 75 X

London: Highfield,
1996

187191275X

Printed by Garnett Dickinson Print Limited

Introduction

Every year thousands of people suffer from food-borne illness, usually involving severe diarrhoea, vomiting and stomach cramps, as a result of eating or drinking contaminated or poisonous food. Many attacks go unreported and it is estimated that one person in fifty will be affected annually. Some of these, especially the very young, the elderly or the infirm will die.

FOOD POISONING TRENDS IN ENGLAND AND WALES (1986-1995)

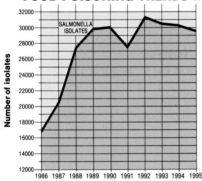
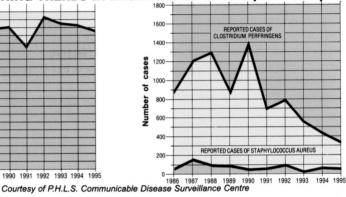

Courtesy of P.H.L.S. Communicable Disease Surveillance Centre

The cost of food poisoning can be high, not only to the country through working days lost, but also to employers and employees engaged in food handling. The owners of premises implicated in food poisoning will lose business and employees may lose their jobs. Food handlers who contravene food legislation may be prosecuted and an outbreak of food poisoning could cost firms responsible thousands of pounds in damage

THE TEN MAIN REASONS FOR FOOD POISONING

1 Food prepared too far in advance and stored at room temperature, i.e. not under refrigeration

2 Cooling food too slowly prior to refrigeration

3 Not reheating food to high enough temperatures to destroy food poisoning bacteria

4 The use of cooked food contaminated with food poisoning bacteria

5 Undercooking

6 Not thawing frozen poultry for sufficient time

7 Cross-contamination from raw food to cooked food

8 Storing hot food below 63°C

9 Infected food handlers

10 Use of leftovers

By courtesy of Dr. D. Roberts, Food Hygiene Laboratory, Central Public Health Laboratory, Colindale.

claims. Negligent food handlers may poison themselves or even worse be responsible for the death of a person consuming food which they have prepared.

Rigorous enforcement of existing food hygiene legislation is important but is not, in itself, sufficient to prevent food poisoning. Food poisoning is normally caused by negligence or ignorance and consequently most experts in food hygiene believe that a reduction in the current depressing statistics can only be achieved by the education of food handlers. One mistake by an untrained food handler in the most modern food premises can cause a serious outbreak of food poisoning.

To be effective, principles of food hygiene should be taught systematically as an important part of early training. Hygiene should become a way of life for all food handlers as soon as they embark on their careers as, once ingrained, bad habits are most difficult to change.

At the end of each section a number of key questions are asked. If you can answer these questions you will be well on the way to passing any of the current basic hygiene examinations. More importantly, if you apply this knowledge in your food business and operate in accordance with the principles laid down in this booklet you should not be responsible for causing a food poisoning outbreak.

All food handlers should receive hygiene training

After reading this book you should:

1	know the causes of food poisoning;
2	know how to prevent food poisoning;
3	be aware of the standards of personal hygiene required by food handlers;
4	know how to use refrigerators and freezers correctly;
5	understand stock rotation;
6	know how to dispose of waste safely and properly;
7	know the common pests found in food premises and how they can be controlled;
8	understand the correct cleaning procedures;
9	understand how food legislation affects you.

Food hygiene

Defining food hygiene

Food hygiene is more than just cleanliness; it includes all practices involved in:

1   protecting food from risk of contamination, including harmful bacteria, poisons and foreign bodies;

2   preventing any bacteria present multiplying to an extent which would result in the illness of consumers or the early spoilage of the food;

3   destroying any harmful bacteria in the food by thorough cooking or processing.

The cost of poor hygiene:

1   food poisoning outbreaks and sometimes death;

2   food contamination and customer complaints;

3   pest infestations;

4   waste food due to spoilage;

5   the closure of food premises by local authority action;

6   fines and costs of legal action taken because of contraventions in hygiene legislation, or because of the sale of unfit or unsatisfactory food;

7   civil action taken by food poisoning sufferers;

8   loss of production and food which has to be destroyed;

9   decontamination cleaning and replacement of damaged equipment.

Poor hygiene can result in food complaints, illness and fines

All of these factors will contribute to a lowering of profits. If the commercial viability of the premises is threatened, employees may lose overtime, bonuses or even their jobs. It is therefore in the best interests of everyone involved in the preparation and handling of food to observe the highest standards of food hygiene.

The benefits of good hygiene:

1   satisfied customers, a good reputation and increased business;

2   compliance with the law;

3   increased shelf-life of food;

4   good working conditions, higher staff morale and lower staff turnover, which promote increased productivity.

All of these factors will contribute to higher profits.

Bacteria

Bacteria are microscopic organisms, often referred to as germs, which are found everywhere, including on and in man, on food, in water, soil and air.

Most bacteria are harmless and some are essential, for example for breaking down decaying matter, or in cheese and yoghurt manufacture. However, a small number of bacteria cause food spoilage and some, known as pathogens, are responsible for causing illness. Several food poisoning bacteria produce toxins (poisons) either in the food or inside the body.

The number of bacteria present in food may be used to determine whether or not the food has been handled correctly.

Bacteria exist everywhere

It is impracticable to operate a food business without food poisoning bacteria being present at one time or another. It is therefore essential that they are denied the conditions which would allow them to reproduce to a level where they present a risk to customers.

Requirements for bacterial growth

Bacteria responsible for causing food poisoning need the following conditions to enable them to grow and, in some cases, produce toxins.

Warmth

The best temperature for the growth of most food poisoning bacteria is 37°C (body temperature), although they can grow quite quickly between 20°C and 50°C. To prevent their growth we must ensure that the temperature of food is kept below 5°C or above 63°C. The temperature range of 5°C to 63°C is often referred to as the **"danger zone".**

Food poisoning bacteria reproduce rapidly in warm food rooms, but most will not grow in a refrigerator (1°C to 4°C) and none in frozen food (−18°C), although many will survive and reproduce on thawing.

Some bacteria are able to produce spores which protect them against adverse conditions such as high temperatures, drying and disinfection. Spores are a resting phase and they do not multiply. When favourable conditions return the spore releases the bacterium which can then start to grow and multiply.

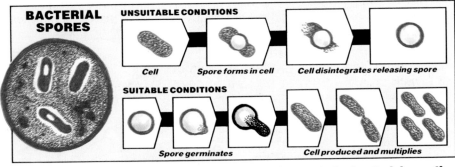

BACTERIAL SPORES

UNSUITABLE CONDITIONS

Cell — Spore forms in cell — Cell disintegrates releasing spore

SUITABLE CONDITIONS

Spore germinates — Cell produced and multiplies

Food and moisture

High protein foods are preferred, especially meat, poultry and dairy produce. Foods such as dried egg or milk powder do not provide the conditions necessary for growth. However, once water or milk is added to the powder, any bacteria present will start growing. It is essential, therefore, to use such food as soon as possible after adding water.

Other foods which do not support bacterial growth are those containing high concentrations of sugar, salt, acid or other preservatives.

Requirements for bacterial growth

WARMTH

TIME

FOOD/MOISTURE

Time

Given the right conditions of food, moisture and warmth, some bacteria can divide into two every ten minutes. This process is known as binary fission. If there is sufficient time, a few bacteria can multiply to such an extent that there are enough present to cause food poisoning. For this reason it is essential that high-risk foods are not left in the **danger zone for longer than is absolutely necessary.**

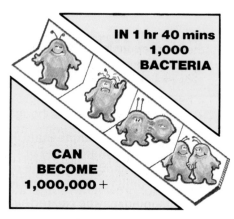

IN 1 hr 40 mins
1,000
BACTERIA

CAN
BECOME
1,000,000 +

High-risk foods

High-risk foods are usually considered as those which support the multiplication of harmful bacteria and are intended for consumption without treatment such as cooking, which would destroy such organisms. These foods are usually proteins and require refrigerated storage. They must always be kept apart from raw foods. Examples include:

1	all cooked meat and poultry;
2	cooked meat products including gravy and stock;
3	milk, cream, artificial cream, custards and dairy produce;
4	cooked eggs and products made from eggs, for example, mayonnaise;
5	shellfish and other seafoods;
6	cooked rice.

All of the above are frequently implicated in outbreaks of food poisoning, especially poultry, raw egg products and cooked meat. Unfortunately contaminated food usually looks, tastes and smells completely normal and cannot be detected without laboratory examination.

What are bacteria, toxins and spores?
Where are food poisoning bacteria found?
What types of bacteria are important to the food industry?
What are the requirements for bacterial growth?
What are high-risk foods?

Food poisoning and food-borne diseases

Food poisoning

Food poisoning is an unpleasant illness which usually occurs within 1 to 36 hours of eating contaminated or poisonous food. Symptoms normally last from 1 to 7 days and include one or more of the following: abdominal pain, diarrhoea, vomiting, nausea and fever.

Food poisoning may be caused by:

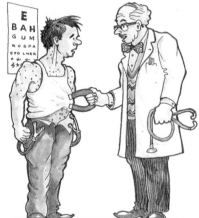

"As I thought! Definitely metallic poisoning"

1. bacteria or their toxins;
2. viruses;
3. chemicals such as insecticides and weedkillers;
4. metals such as lead, copper and mercury;
5. poisonous plants such as deadly nightshade and toadstools.

Bacterial food poisoning is by far the commonest and in some instances may result in death. A large number of bacteria are usually involved and this requires them to multiply within the food.

Common food poisoning bacteria

Salmonella

Source	Raw foods, especially meat, poultry, milk and eggs, carriers, pets, rodents, birds, flies, terrapins and sewage.
Onset period	6 to 72 hours (usually 12 to 36 hours).
Symptoms	Abdominal pain, diarrhoea, vomiting and fever which usually lasts for 1 to 7 days.
Mode of spread to high-risk food	Direct contact with contaminated raw food or indirectly via work surfaces, utensils, wiping cloths and hands. The liquid from thawing poultry and meat is particularly hazardous. Pests, droppings and urine can all contaminate food. Undercooking and/or warm storage of poultry and meat will allow survival and multiplication of *salmonella* if present.

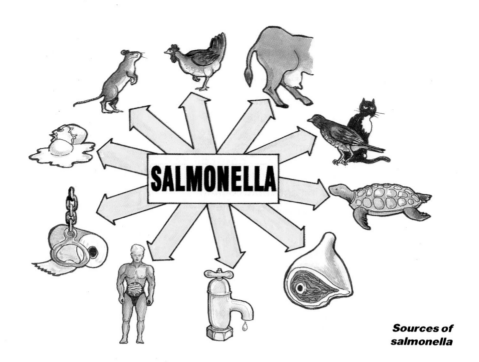

Sources of salmonella

Control	Strict personal hygiene, segregate work areas, surfaces, utensils and operatives handling raw and high-risk food. Separate areas for thawing and cooling food. Thorough cooking of food (to the centre). Refrigerated storage. Improve farm and slaughterhouse hygiene. Safe sewage disposal and chlorination of water. Excluding pests and pets. Training of food handlers and strict temperature control.
Important characteristics	Some types of *salmonella* can cause food poisoning with very small numbers. Responsible for >95% of reported cases of bacterial food poisoning.*

*Excluding campylobacter

Clostridium perfringens

Source	Animal and human excreta, soil (on vegetables), dust, raw meat/poultry, flies, cockroaches and other insects.
Onset period	8 to 22 hours (usually 12 to 18).
Symptoms	Abdominal pain and diarrhoea, vomiting is rare. Illness usually lasts 12 to 48 hours.

Mode of spread to high-risk food	Direct contact with contaminated raw meat or vegetables or indirectly via work surfaces, equipment, wiping cloths and hands. Inadequate cooking (or reheating) followed by slow cooling is the major problem.
Control	Strict personal hygiene and good hygiene practices. Separation of raw and high-risk foods. Strict temperature control especially thorough cooking and rapid cooling. Training of food handlers.
Important characteristics	Produces spores which protect the bacteria at high temperatures. Can multiply every 10 minutes at around 45°C. Does not like oxygen. Responsible for <5% of reported cases of food poisoning.

Sources of Clostridium perfringens

Staphylococcus aureus

Source	Human nose, mouth, skin, boils and cuts. Raw milk from cows or goats.
Onset period	1 to 6 hours.
Symptoms	Abdominal pain, vomiting, prostration and subnormal temperatures. Usually lasts 6 to 24 hours.
Mode of spread to high-risk food	Usually via the hands after touching the nose, mouth, hair, septic cuts or spots.
Control	Avoid handling food directly. Good personal hygiene especially regarding handwashing. Use of waterproof dressings. Exclude operatives with boils and septic cuts or who are sneezing and coughing. Rapid cooling and refrigeration of high-risk foods. Training of food handlers.

Sources of Staphylococcus aureus

Important characteristics	Produces a toxin (poison) in food which is difficult to destroy by normal cooking temperatures. Responsible for <1% of reported cases of food poisoning.

Food-borne diseases

Other bacterial illnesses which can be transmitted via food include typhoid, paratyphoid, tuberculosis, dysentery and brucellosis. However, unlike bacterial food poisoning, only small numbers of bacteria are required to cause the illness; a multiplication of bacteria within the food is not necessary.

The bacteria responsible are found, among other places, in man's intestines and the chain of infection is the same as that involved in food poisoning, i.e.

BACTERIA IN FAECES → TRANSFERRED VIA HANDS OR SEWAGE → TO FOOD → CONSUMED → ILLNESS IN MAN

Two types of bacteria causing food-borne disease which are of particular note are campylobacter, which is responsible for more cases of illness than *salmonella,* and listeria which is able to multiply below 3°C, albeit very slowly.

Sewage contamination of food can result in food-borne illness

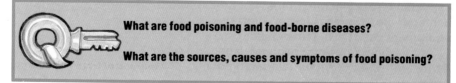

What are food poisoning and food-borne diseases?

What are the sources, causes and symptoms of food poisoning?

Food contamination

To prevent the consumption of unsound and unsafe food it is essential that contamination of high-risk food is kept to a minimum.

There are three types of contamination of high-risk food:

(1) bacterial contamination – which usually occurs within food premises because of ignorance, inadequate space, poor design or because of food handlers taking short cuts. Contamination of this sort is the most serious and may result in food spoilage, food poisoning or even death;

(2) physical contamination – by foreign bodies which may be dangerous, for example glass or nails, but is normally unpleasant and a nuisance.

(3) Chemical contamination – from pesticides, waste or cleaning chemicals. Food should never be stored near poisonous chemicals, and such chemicals should never be stored in empty food containers.

Sources of food poisoning bacteria

(1) The person People commonly harbour food poisoning bacteria in the nose, mouth, intestine and also on the skin. Food may be contaminated directly by the hands, sneezing or coughing, or indirectly by sewage contaminated water. All water used in food premises should be suitably treated, for example by chlorination. The Aberdeen typhoid outbreak was due to cans of Argentinian corned beef which had been cooled in sewage-polluted water.

(2) Raw food Raw food is particularly hazardous, especially red meat, poultry (up to 80% of frozen birds may carry *salmonella*), untreated milk, eggs and shellfish such as oysters. Raw food should always be kept separate from high-risk food. The liquid from defrosting foods, especially frozen poultry, must not be allowed to contaminate wiping cloths, high-risk food or equipment used for high-risk food.

Soil harbours harmful bacteria, and care must be taken when bringing vegetables into food rooms.

(3) Insects Several insects may transmit food poisoning bacteria to food. Flies and cockroaches present the greatest hazard because of their feeding habits and the sites which they visit. Flies often land on animal faeces where they pick up large numbers of bacteria on their hairy bodies. In addition they defecate and vomit previous meals back onto the food as they feed.

Careless use of insecticide may result in dead insects ending up in food.

Cockroaches often live in sewers and commonly feed on infected waste. They hide in the most inaccessible places in food rooms and may carry food poisoning organisms on their legs and bodies to food and equipment on which they walk.

(4) Rodents Both rats and mice commonly excrete organisms such as salmonellae. Contamination of food may occur from droppings, urine, hairs and gnawing. Food-contact surfaces on which rodents have walked must be disinfected before use. Food suspected of being contaminated by rodents must be destroyed.

(5) Dust There are always large numbers of bacteria in dust and floating about in the air. Open food should always be covered when cleaning is carried out, especially dusting and sweeping.

(6) Refuse and waste food Waste and unfit food must not be allowed to accumulate in food rooms. Care must be taken to avoid contamination of food from waste either directly or indirectly. Food operatives must wash their hands after handling refuse. Refuse receptacles are a favourite breeding place for flies and must always have tight-fitting lids which are replaced after use.

Sources of food poisoning bacteria

(7) Animals and birds Both domestic and wild animals are known to carry harmful bacteria on their bodies and in their intestines. Furthermore, dirt can be transferred to food from their feet, and hairs and feathers may end up in the food. Pets must always be kept out of food rooms. Terrapins are occasionally implicated in cases of food poisoning through contact with infected water. Other incidents have occurred because of contamination of food by bird droppings.

Vehicles and routes of bacterial contamination

Sometimes, harmful bacteria pass directly from the source to high-risk food, but, as bacteria are usually static and the sources may not be in direct contact with food, the bacteria rely on other things to transfer them to food. These things are known as **vehicles** and the main ones are:

1	hands;	**2**	cloths and equipment;
3	hand-contact surfaces;	**4**	food-contact surfaces.

Indirect contamination using an intermediate vehicle is by far the commonest, for example the passage of bacteria from the intestine of a food handler to food via the hands, after using the toilet. Where contamination is passed from raw food to high-risk food via, for example a worktop, this is known as **cross-contamination**. The path which bacteria use to transfer from the source to the food is known as the **route**.

SOURCES, VEHICLES AND ROUTES OF CONTAMINATION

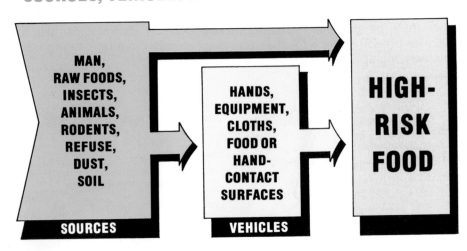

MAN, RAW FOODS, INSECTS, ANIMALS, RODENTS, REFUSE, DUST, SOIL

SOURCES

HANDS, EQUIPMENT, CLOTHS, FOOD OR HAND-CONTACT SURFACES

VEHICLES

HIGH-RISK FOOD

Physical contamination

Foreign bodies found in food may be brought into food premises with the raw materials or introduced during storage, preparation, service or display.

Although there are many different types of foreign bodies, it is essential that managers are aware of those commonly found in their particular sector of the food industry and that they exercise all due diligence to secure their removal or prevent their introduction. Food handlers must observe all company rules and take appropriate precautions to ensure that they are not responsible for the contamination of food. Foreign bodies which often result in food complaints include:

1	bolts, nuts, wire, staples and other pieces of metal – often found after maintenance and repair work;
2	cardboard, string and polythene – often introduced from packaging;
3	rodents, rodent hairs, insects, feathers and droppings;
4	sweet papers and cigarette ends;
5	items from personnel such as earrings, fingernails, hair, buttons, pentops, soiled bandages and plasters;
6	glass;
7	cleaning materials;
8	mould;
9	wood splinters;
10	grease and oil;
11	flaking paint or rust.

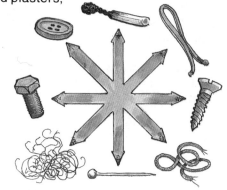

Contaminated raw materials must not be accepted by a food business, if after normal sorting, they would still be unfit for human consumption.
Food must be so stored and protected to minimize any risk of contamination. Hazardous and/or inedible substances must be labelled and stored in secure containers.
It is an offence to sell food which is unsafe or not of the nature, substance or quality demanded by the purchaser.

What is food contamination and what types exist?
What are the sources, vehicles and routes of contamination?
List examples of physical contaminants?

The prevention of food poisoning

In most cases of food poisoning a chain of events takes place and, if we are to reduce the incidence of illness, this chain must be broken.

There are three main ways of breaking the food poisoning chain:

1 protecting food from contamination;
2 preventing any bacteria within food from multiplying;
3 destroying those bacteria present within the food.

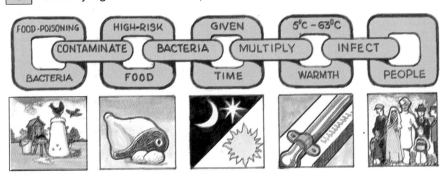

Protecting food from contamination by:

1 Keeping food covered wherever possible;
2 Not using unsuitable, defective or dirty equipment;
3 not using dirty wiping cloths. Disposable cloths are preferable;
4 only handling food when unavoidable. Tongs, plates and trays should be used in preference to hands;

Avoid handling food

5	separating raw and cooked food at all stages of preparation, storage and distribution. The same equipment and working surface must not be used to handle raw and high-risk foods;
6	preventing insects, animals and birds from entering food rooms or coming into contact with food;
7	storing food in rodent-proof containers and ensuring that the lids are tightly replaced after use;
8	maintaining the highest standards of personal hygiene at all times;
9	all food handlers wearing suitable protective clothing;
10	not handling parts of crockery or cutlery that come into contact with food, for example knife blades or inside glasses and cups;
11	removing unfit or waste food and refuse promptly and keeping them apart from high-risk food;
12	keeping food and equipment off the floor;
13	ensuring that the liquid from thawed frozen meat and poultry does not come into contact with high-risk food or surfaces and equipment used for high-risk food;
14	using the correct cleaning and disinfection procedures;
15	not using wash-hand basins for washing food or food equipment and not using food sinks for hand washing;
16	purchasing food from reputable sources.

Food should
NOT
be washed in facilities provided for personal hygiene

Preventing any bacteria within food from multiplying by:

1. storing food out of the **danger zone.** Food should be kept below 5°C, for example in a refrigerator, or kept above 63°C, for example in a bain marie;
2. ensuring that during preparation, food is within the **danger zone** for as short a time as possible. High-risk food must not be left in the ambient temperatures of kitchens or serving areas, unless in the course of preparation or needed for immediate consumption;
3. using suitable preservatives such as salt and sugar;
4. not allowing dried foods to absorb moisture.

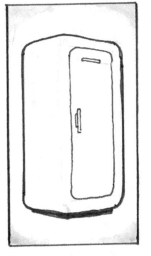

Destroying those bacteria within food by:

1. thorough cooking;
2. heat processing such as pasteurization, sterilization or canning.

A combination of a suitable temperature and sufficient time is always required to destroy bacteria. The time and the temperature required will depend on the particular organism. For example, spores of *Clostridium perfringens* are much more heat resistant than *salmonella* bacteria.

Pasteurization of milk can be as low as 63°C for 30 minutes, whereas the canning of vegetables requires 121°C for three minutes. Cooking temperatures of 75°C should normally be achieved at the centre of food to ensure safety.

How can the food poisoning chain be broken?
How can the contamination of high-risk food be prevented?
How can temperature be used to prevent food poisoning?

The storage, temperature control, preparation, cooking and preservation of food

Food storage

Correct storage of food is fundamental to the hygienic operation of any food business. Failure to ensure satisfactory conditions of cleanliness, temperature, humidity and stock rotation can result in problems of unfit or spoiled food, including mould, discolouration, staleness and insect and rodent infestations.

Storage conditions should ensure that the nutritional value, appearance, taste and fitness of food are of the highest standard. Storage areas must not be overloaded and the available space must be taken into account when purchasing food.

All deliveries should be checked for freshness, temperature, colour, odour, contamination, infestations and satisfactory packaging and labelling. Any problems should be notified to the supervisor. As far as practicable, external packaging should not be brought into food preparation areas.

Dry-food stores

Rooms used for the storage of dried and canned foods should be dry, cool, well-lit, ventilated, vermin-proof and kept clean and tidy. Food should be stored away from the walls and pipes affected by condensate and off the floor on suitable shelves such as tubular stainless steel racks, or in mobile bins. Spillages should be cleared away promptly. All goods should be inspected before placing in storage. Problems encountered include soiled delivery trays, infestations, damaged and leaking cartons, rusty cans and out-of-date stock. If possible, fruit and vegetables should be stored in dry, cool, well-ventilated areas, preferably separate from other food. Fruit should be examined regularly as mould spreads rapidly.

Canned foods

The risk from canned foods is very small compared with the number produced and this safety record will continue if:

Blown cans must not be used

1. blown cans are not used;
2. badly-dented, seam-damaged, holed or rusty cans are rejected;
3. stock rotation is carried out.

The shelf-life of canned foods

	Months
rhubarb, pasteurized solid meat packs (refrigerated)	9
fruit juice, prunes, milk products	12
new potatoes, blackberries, raspberries, plums	18
vegetables, baked beans, soups, ready-meals	24
solid-pack cold meat products and fish in oil	60

After the above times the food will not present a health risk but there may be changes in colour, texture and flavour.

The storage of perishable food

High-risk and perishable foods may be contaminated by harmful bacteria which can multiply to dangerous levels if not stored under refrigeration.

The recent trend to remove additives means that some foods must now be stored under refrigeration when previously they didn't need to be, for example opened bottles of tomato sauce.

> **No food must be kept at temperatures which would result in a risk to health. High-risk food must be kept below 8°C.**

The correct use of refrigerators

The common food poisoning organisms are incapable of multiplying and producing poisons at temperatures below 5°C. Furthermore, the spoilage of food by bacteria and mould is reduced. As can be seen from the "ten main reasons for food poisoning" (page 2), temperature control is the single most important factor in preventing food poisoning. Therefore, it is essential for food handlers to receive clear instructions on the use of refrigerators to ensure that they operate effectively.

Siting

Refrigerators should be sited in well-ventilated areas away from heat sources and the rays of the sun.

Construction

Refrigerators should be constructed to facilitate easy cleaning. Internal linings and shelves should be impervious and non-corroding. Door seals must be maintained in good condition and the unit should be serviced regularly.

Operating temperature

Units should normally operate between 1°C and 4°C. A thermometer should be permanently positioned in the warmest part of the refrigerator and the temperature checked at least three times a day.

Defrosting and cleaning

Refrigerators must not be overloaded

Defrosting and cleaning should be carried out frequently in accordance with the manufacturer's instructions. Units which defrost automatically should still be cleaned at least weekly. Bicarbonate of soda (one tablespoon to a gallon of water) may be used, but perfumed cleaning agents must not.

Packing and stock rotation

Refrigerators must not be overloaded, and food should never be placed in front of cooling units. Only perishable foods should be stored in the refrigerator. This includes vacuum packs and pasteurized cans of meat. Stock rotation is essential to avoid spoilage.

Hot food

Hot food must never be placed directly into a refrigerator if this would raise the temperature of food already being stored above 5°C. It will also encourage condensation and consequently contamination. Joints of meat intended to be eaten cold should be kept below 2½ Kgs (6 lbs) and less than 5 cm thick to facilitate cooling within 1½ hours prior to refrigeration.

Contamination and covering of food

Raw food must always be kept apart from high-risk food. Separate refrigerators are preferred, although, if in the same unit, the raw food must always be placed at the bottom. Food should be covered to prevent drying out, cross-contamination and absorption of odour.

Open cans of food

To avoid the acid attack on opened and part-used cans, they should not be stored in refrigerators, especially such food as fruit, fruit juice or tomatoes. The unused contents should be emptied into a suitable container such as a covered plastic bowl.

Staff training and responsibilities

All food handlers must receive instruction on the correct use of the refrigerator and, in particular, be told to keep the door open for the minimum amount of time. The temperature of refrigerated deliveries should be checked on arrival.

Freezers and frozen food

Commercial freezers should operate at $-18°C$ or slightly below. At this temperature food will keep for a reasonable time with no bacterial growth. However, spores and pathogens will survive and if the temperature rises above $-10°C$, spoilage organisms, especially moulds and yeast, begin to cause problems.

Staff must be trained to use freezers and handle frozen food correctly. The temperature, and packaging, of deliveries of frozen food should be checked before unloading. If the temperature is around $-18°C$ the food should be transferred to the freezer as quickly as possible. Deliveries above $-12°C$ are unacceptable. New stock should always be placed below existing food. Food must not be stored above the freezer load line and must not be kept for longer than recommended by the manufacturer, as the quality gradually deteriorates. Suitable packaging is essential to avoid freezer burn.

A general guide for food kept at $-18°C$ is:	Months
vegetables, fruit, most meat	up to 12
pork, sausages, offal, fish, butter and soft cheese	up to 6

Thawing of frozen food

Most food taken from the freezer can be cooked immediately, but poultry and large joints must be completely thawed before cooking. The manufacturer's instructions should always be followed. Thawing of raw meat/poultry must take place in an area entirely separate from other foods which may be exposed to risk of contamination from thawed liquid. This area must never be used for cooked food which is cooling prior to refrigeration. Thawing is best carried out at 10°C to 15°C or in a thawing cabinet.

Thawing can also be achieved using clean cold running water, below 15°C or in an appropriate microwave oven, although extreme care is necessary because of the risk of uneven heating.

Thawing times in refrigerators vary considerably depending on the temperature, for example a 1.1 Kg bird takes around 70 hours at 1°C, 40 hours at 5°C and 13 hours at 10°C to reach 0°C. Before using a refrigerator for thawing, it is essential to know the temperature of the refrigerator and the time a specific frozen chicken or other food product takes to thaw at that temperature. Extreme care must also be exercised to avoid cross-contamination.

Frozen food must not be thawed near high-risk foods

Rules for handling frozen poultry

1	keep separate from other foods;
2	thaw completely in a cool room. Poultry will be ready for cooking when the body is pliable, the legs are flexible and the body cavity is free from ice crystals;
3	remove giblets;
4	once thawed, keep in the refrigerator and cook within 24 hours;
5	cook thoroughly and cook the stuffing separately;
6	all utensils and surfaces used for the preparation of raw meat and poultry must be thoroughly cleaned and disinfected before being used for high-risk food;
7	eat straight after cooking or, if the bird is to be carved cold, cool it quickly and store in the refrigerator. As with all meats **refrigerated storage is essential within one and a half hours;**
8	avoid handling the cooked bird.

THAWING AND COOKING TIMES OF FROZEN POULTRY	Oven ready weight Kg (lbs)	Approx. thawing time at room temp. hours	Min. cooking time at 180°C/350°F Gas 4. (in foil) hours
	2.25 (5)	15	$2\frac{1}{2}$
	4.5 (10)	18	$3\frac{1}{2}$
	6.75 (15)	24	$4\frac{3}{4}$
	9.0 (20)	30	$5\frac{3}{4}$

These are minimum times. The bird is cooked when the juices run clear.

Stock rotation

Satisfactory rotation of stock, to ensure that older food is used first, is essential to avoid spoilage. Stock rotation applies to all types of food. Daily checks should be made on short-life perishable food stored in refrigerators, whereas weekly examination of other foods may suffice.

Stock which is undisturbed for long periods will encourage rodent and insect infestations. Good stock rotation has the added advantage of assisting in the maintenance of the correct levels of stock.

Stock rotation has been much easier since the advent of open-date coding. Food handlers should adopt their own code to identify the date of delivery of products not requiring a "use-by" date. Remember the rule: **"First in, first out"**.

Most food must be labelled to indicate the "use-by" or "best before" date, together with details of any special storage conditions, for example keep under refrigeration.

Food preparation

The observance of good hygiene practices during food preparation is an important element in preventing food poisoning. Raw food and high-risk food should be prepared in different areas with separate, clean equipment. Raw food should be washed thoroughly in a separate sink which is not used for washing utensils etc. and is positioned to avoid cross-contamination of high-risk food or clean utensils/equipment. Disposable wiping cloths should be used.

The handling of food should be minimized and it must not be left in warm, humid atmospheres. Food handlers should work in a logical, planned manner ensuring that working surfaces are kept as tidy as possible. Spillages and waste food should be cleared away promptly.

Cooking

Thorough cooking is important to destroy harmful bacteria, although some will produce toxins which will withstand boiling for at least 30 minutes. Spores may also survive cooking. Although some processed, canned and bottled food may only require reheating to make the food palatable, raw and most frozen and chilled food will require thorough cooking. A minimum centre temperature of 75°C will usually be required and this should be checked with a probe thermometer. After cooking, the food should be eaten as soon as possible. Food being reheated for immediate consumption should be heated to at least 82°C and this is a legal requirement in Scotland.

Microwave cooking

Microwave ovens are a safe and effective method of cooking and heating food provided that instructions are followed. The destruction of food poisoning organisms is based on a combination of high temperatures and sufficient time and it is essential to know the power (wattage) of the oven to ensure adequate time is allowed to achieve the temperatures to ensure the safety of the food. Food should usually be heated throughout to 75°C and this should be checked in several places, using a probe thermometer, to guard against the possibility of cold spots. Stirring of liquids may be required and standing time may also be necessary on completion of cooking.

If food is to be kept hot prior to serving, it must be maintained above 63°C.

Refrigerated display units are essential

Serving

Serving utensils must be stored properly, especially ice-cream scoops. Food placed on tables, such as bread rolls, must not be re-used. All plates and utensils must be clean and dry, and those parts likely to come into contact with high-risk food should not be handled. Condiments should be kept in clean containers, covered where necessary.

Customers should not be able to handle open food. Food should be pre-wrapped, covered or protected with sneeze screens. High-risk food should be kept in refrigerated display units. Counters in retail outlets should not be used for food storage or preparation.

Cooling

Food which is to be refrigerated should be cooled quickly and placed in the refrigerator within $1\frac{1}{2}$ hours of cooking. It is better to use smaller joints of meat as they cool more rapidly. Liquids should be poured into clean, shallow pans and stirred frequently. Cooling is best carried out using a blast chiller, a cold room or an iced water bath.

Food must not be left in the danger zone of temperature

Rewarming of refrigerated meat dishes is bad practice. If food is reheated, it must be cooked thoroughly, to a core temperature of at least 82°C, for immediate consumption. Any reheated food must be discarded, not used later.

The time between: refrigeration and cooking (or processing); cooking and eating; cooking and refrigeration; refrigeration and serving; must be kept as short as possible.

Food preservation

Preservation is the treatment of food to prevent or delay spoilage and destroy or inhibit the growth of pathogenic organisms which would render the food unfit. Often a combination of techniques is used, for example cooking followed by refrigeration. Food may be preserved by the use of:

1	high temperatures (pasteurization, sterilization, cooking and canning);
2	low temperatures (refrigeration and freezing);
3	dehydration (the removal of moisture);
4	chemicals (salt, sugar, acids and sulphur dioxide);
5	vacuum packing (sous vide) and
6	physical methods (irradiation and smoking).

Why is correct storage and stock rotation of food important?
What are the essential features of a dry-food store?
What are the important rules regarding the safe use of refrigerators?
What are the important rules relating to the storage of frozen food?
What are the risks associated with the thawing of frozen food?
What are the main risks involved with the preparation, cooking, serving and cooling of food?
What are the main ways of preserving food?

Personal hygiene

Most people carry some type of food poisoning organism at one time or another, and food handlers have a moral and legal responsibility to observe high standards of personal cleanliness to ensure that they do not contaminate food.

Hands and skin

As the hands are in direct contact with food, they are the main route for transferring food poisoning bacteria. Hands must be kept very clean at all times. The correct hand washing procedure is essential. A non-hand operated warm water spray is preferred. Alternatively the wash hand basin should be filled with hand hot water. The hands should be wet and a liquid soap applied. A good lather is required and the wrists, forearms and in between the fingers should all receive attention. Where necessary, for example after visiting the toilet or handling raw food, a clean nailbrush should be used to scrub the nails. The hands should be rinsed and dried. Efficient drying of hands may be achieved by using disposable paper towels, which can be used to turn off the tap, hot air dryers or continuous roller towels.

Food handlers must wash their hands regularly throughout the working day and especially:

1 after visiting the w.c.;
2 on entering the food room and before handling any food or equipment;
3 in between handling raw and cooked food;
4 after combing or touching the hair;
5 after eating, smoking, coughing or blowing the nose;
6 after handling waste food or refuse;
7 after handling cleaning chemicals.

As fingernails may harbour bacteria, they must be kept short and clean. Nail varnish may contaminate food and should not be used. People who continually put their fingers in their mouth, for example nail biters, should not be employed as food handlers. Licking the fingers before picking up sheets of wrapping paper is a particularly bad habit.

The nose, mouth and ears

Up to 40 per cent of adults carry staphylococci in the nose and mouth. Coughs and sneezes can carry droplet infection for a considerable distance and persons with bad colds should not handle open food. Disposable single-use paper tissues are preferable to handkerchiefs. Picking or scratching the nose is not acceptable.

As the mouth is likely to harbour staphylococci, food handlers should not eat sweets, chew gum, taste food with the finger or an unwashed spoon or blow into glasses to polish them. Apart from being aesthetically unacceptable, spitting can obviously result in food contamination and is illegal.

Discharges from the ears, eyes and nose may contaminate food and employees must report these ailments to their supervisor. Medical clearance to start work will normally be required.

Cuts, boils, whitlows and septic spots

Cuts, spots and sores provide an ideal place for bacterial multiplication. To prevent con-tamination of food by harmful bacteria and blood, these lesions should be completely covered by waterproof dressings, preferably coloured blue or green to aid detection if they became detached. Cuts on fingers may need the extra protection of waterproof fingerstalls. Waterproof dressings will also assist in pre-venting cuts going septic.

Food handlers with colds, boils and septic cuts must not handle food.

Jewellery and perfume

Food handlers should not wear earrings, watches, jewelled rings or brooches, as they harbour dirt and bacteria. Furthermore, stones and small pieces of metal may end up in the food and result in a customer complaint.

Strong-smelling perfume or aftershave should not be worn by food handlers, as it may taint foods, especially those with a high fat content.

The hair

Hair is constantly falling out and, along with dandruff, can result in contamination of food. Furthermore, the scalp often contains harmful bacteria and must be shampooed regularly. Food handlers should wear suitable head covering which completely encloses the hair. Hair-nets worn under turbans, helmets and hats are recommended. Combing of hair and adjustments to head covering should only take place in cloakrooms and should not be carried out whilst wearing protective clothing, as hairs may end up on the shoulders and then in the product.

Smoking

It is illegal to use snuff and tobacco, including cigarettes, pipes or cigars, in food rooms or whilst handling open food. Not only is this to prevent cigarette ends and ash contaminating food but also because:

1 people touch their lips whilst smoking and they may transfer harmful bacteria to food;
2 smoking encourages coughing and droplet infection;
3 cigarette ends contaminated with saliva are placed on working surfaces;
4 an unpleasant environment may be created for non-smokers.

The only place to smoke in a food premises should be the rest room.

Protective clothing

Persons handling open food, other than raw vegetables and drinks, must wear clean and washable overclothing, preferably light-coloured without external pockets. Press studs or velcrose fastening are preferable to buttons. Protective garments should be appropriate for the work being carried out and should completely cover ordinary clothing. Jumper and shirt sleeves must not protrude and, if short-sleeved overalls are worn, only clean forearms must be visible. Suitable footwear should be worn to prevent slipping and to protect the feet.

Staff must be aware that protective clothing is worn to protect the food from risk of contamination and not to keep their own clothes clean. Dust, pet hairs and woollen fibres are just a few of the contaminants carried on ordinary clothing. Protective clothing should not be worn outside the food premises, not used to travel to and from work and not worn during lunch time sporting activities such as football.

Outdoor clothing and personal effects must not be brought into food rooms unless stored in suitable lockers. Protective clothing should not be hung in sanitary accommodation.

General health and reporting of illness

Food handlers should be in good health in all aspects from oral hygiene to general fitness. Any food handlers suffering from diarrhoea, vomiting or a food-borne infection must not handle food. They must notify their supervisor who must exclude them from any work which would expose food to risks from pathogens. Food handlers who have consumed a meal known to have caused food poisoning or live in the same household as a confirmed case or have suffered from diarrhoea or vomiting whilst abroad should also report to the supervisor. Food handlers who excrete food poisoning organisms must not resume food handling duties without medical clearance.

Persons with skin infections, sores, heavy colds and ear or eye discharge should be excluded until medical clearance has been obtained.

Hygiene training

All food handlers must receive the appropriate supervision and instruction and/or hygiene training to ensure that they are aware of the hygiene hazards associated with their job and the safety of food produced. This will include induction training, hygiene awareness instruction and/or attending appropriate formal courses

Food handlers must maintain high standards of personal hygiene and wear suitable clean and where appropriate, protective clothing.

Food handlers who are suffering from a food-borne disease or have an infected wound or skin condition must not be allowed to work in any food handling area if they are likely to contaminate food with pathogens.

Food handlers so afflicted must report to the proprietor of the food business.

Why is personal hygiene important in preventing food poisoning?
When must food handlers wash their hands?
How can food handlers contaminate food?
When should food handlers report illness to their supervisor?
What are the important properties of protective clothing?

The construction and design of food premises

Site selection

The selection of a suitable site is most important when planning food premises. Consideration must be given to the provision and availability of services, i.e. electricity, gas, water supply and effluent disposal and the accessibility for delivery and refuse collection. The possibility of flooding and pollution must also be considered.

Design of food premises

After obtaining planning permission, the following design principles should be followed:

1. cross-contamination should be eliminated; clean and dirty processes must be separated. Work areas should be colour coded;

2. work flow should be continuous and progress in a uniform direction from raw material to finished product;

3. suitable and sufficient facilities for personal hygiene, cleaning and disinfecting equipment and washing food must be provided, together with adequate supplies of hot and clean, wholesome cold water. Hot water should be around 60°C, cold water less than 10°C and warm water from spray taps around 49°C. Wash hand basins should be positioned close to work stations.

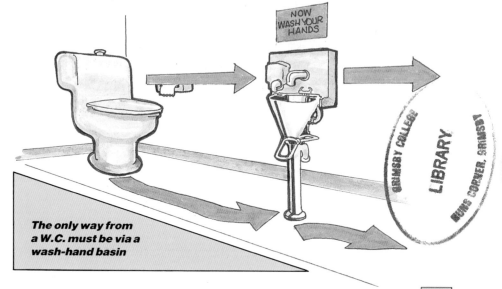

The only way from a W.C. must be via a wash-hand basin

4	adequate refrigeration, cooking and cooling facilities must be provided. Flexible gas pipes should be used to allow movement of equipment for cleaning. Electrical supplies should be fitted with accessible cut out switches. Trailing wires must be avoided. Waterproof sockets are preferred;
5	the premises must be capable of being thoroughly cleaned;
6	insects, rodents and birds must be denied access;
7	suitable staff facilities must be provided including appropriate sanitary conveniences, separated from food rooms by ventilated spaces. Public sanitary accommodation must be provided in restaurants, cafes and public houses;
8	adequate drainage capable of removing peak loads quickly without flooding must be provided;
9	suitable and sufficient ventilation is necessary to ensure reasonable working conditions and reduce temperatures and humidities. Steam and heat producing appliances require suitable canopies;
10	high standards of lighting are necessary to facilitate cleaning and provide safe and satisfactory working conditions. Lighting systems should not produce shadows or glare and fluorescent tubes should be protected by diffusers.

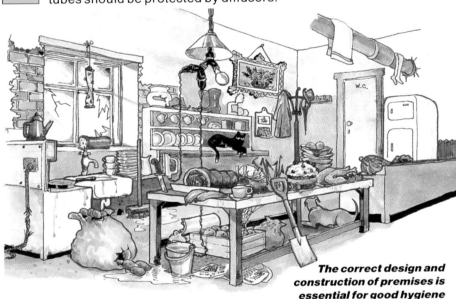

The correct design and construction of premises is essential for good hygiene

Construction details

Ceilings

Ceilings should be smooth, fire resistant, durable, light-coloured, coved at wall joints and easy to clean.

Wall finishes
Finishes should be smooth, impervious, non-flaking, durable, light-coloured and capable of being thoroughly cleaned. Surfaces may need to be resistant to spillages, chemicals, grease, heat and impact. Internal walls should be solid, as cavities provide harbourage for pests.

Floor surfaces
Surfaces should be durable, non-absorbent, anti-slip, without crevices and capable of being effectively cleaned. They may need to be resistant to acids, grease and salts, and should slope sufficiently for liquids to drain to trapped gullies. The angle between walls and floors should be coved.

Windows and doors
Windows, if present, should be fixed on north-facing walls to reduce glare and solar heat gain. If there is a risk of infestation, opening windows must be fitted with cleansable fly-screens. Where appropriate, external doors should be screened and doors should be self-closing.

Wooden finishes
Wood should not normally be used but if unavoidable, for example window frames, it should be well-seasoned, properly knotted, stopped and primed and given three coats of polyurethane paint.

The storage and disposal of waste
Suitable receptacles should be provided, both inside and outside food premises, for the disposal of waste food and debris. Disposable polythene sacks or plastic bins are usually provided for internal use and dustbins or skips for external use. Dustbins must have tight-fitting lids. Compactors which completely enclose the refuse are preferred.

Keep refuse areas tidy

Refuse containers used internally must be emptied as frequently as necessary and always at the end of the day. After emptying, reusable containers must be thoroughly cleaned before being brought back into the food room. Waste-disposal units are commonly used for removing food debris.

Receptacles used for storage or collection of refuse should not be reused for the storage of food.

Empty food containers which are intended for reuse, for example bottles and trays, must be protected from contamination, especially by dogs. It is preferable to store such containers in a suitable room or well clear of the floor under a lean-to.

External refuse areas must be kept clean and tidy so as not to attract rodents, birds and insects. Receptacles must be emptied as frequently as necessary and the yard surface must be hosed down regularly to avoid creating a nuisance. After emptying, waste receptacles should be rinsed out. Hands must always be washed after emptying refuse containers and handling waste.

Trade waste agreements should be made with the local authority or a reputable company.

Food premises must be kept clean and maintained in good repair and condition.

The layout, design and construction must permit good hygiene practices and, where necessary, suitable temperature conditions for processing and storage must be provided.

Adequate numbers of suitably located wash-hand basins with hot and cold (or mixed) water, soap and drying facilities must be provided.

Adequate, well ventilated toilet facilities which do not lead into food rooms must be available.

Suitable and sufficient ventilation and lighting must be provided.

Floor, wall and food contact surfaces of food rooms must be easy to clean and, where necessary, disinfect. They will usually need to be made of impervious, washable non-toxic materials.

Where necessary, facilities for cleaning and disinfecting equipment and washing food must be provided and kept clean.

Food waste and refuse must not accumulate in food rooms, and must be deposited in suitable, closable containers.

Adequate provision must be made for the removal and storage of food-waste and refuse.

An adequate supply of potable (drinking) water must be provided.

Equipment for food handling

All equipment, working surfaces and other utensils which are used in food premises should be designed and constructed to minimize harbourage of soils, bacteria or pests, and to enable them to be thoroughly cleaned and disinfected. Surfaces in contact with food should be smooth, impervious, non-toxic, non-flaking, corrosion-resistant, durable and suitable for their intended use. Resistance to heat and attack by acid foods, such as fruit juices and milk, may need to be considered. Cracked, chipped, broken and badly-pitted equipment harbours dirt and bacteria, and should not be used.

Food-grade stainless steel is appropriate for most equipment. Wooden surfaces should not be used, as they are absorbent and incapable of being cleaned and disinfected. Cutting boards and handles of knives and brushes may be made from polypropylene or other suitable synthetic material. Tubular stainless steel is preferred to painted or galvanized angle iron.

The use of different colours or shapes as a code to ensure equipment used for raw food is not used for high-risk food is recommended.

Where practicable, and with due regard to safety, equipment should be mobile to facilitate its removal for cleaning. This is particularly important if sited close to walls. All guards must be capable of being thoroughly cleaned.

Wooden, dirty and defective equipment must not be used

Food equipment must be kept clean and made of such materials and kept in such condition as to minimize the risk of contamination of food.

Equipment must be kept clean

How can the correct design of food premises prevent cross-contamination?
What facilities are required for personal hygiene and for cleaning food and equipment?
Why must food premises be well-constructed and kept in good repair?
What provision must be made for the safe disposal of waste?
What provision should be made for effective temperature control?
What are the important properties of food equipment?

Pest control

·A **food pest** is an animal which lives in or on man's food and is destructive, noxious or troublesome. Food pests, including dogs, cats and other pets, are a source of food poisoning organisms and must be kept out of food premises. Pests contaminate food with hair, fur, droppings, eggs and dead bodies. Flies vomit on food during feeding and may have just left a pile of refuse or animal faeces before visiting your premises. Food rooms must always be kept clean and proofed against entry of pests.

The common pests found in the food industry include:

1. rodents: rats and mice;
2. insects: flies, wasps, cockroaches, psocids, silverfish, stored product insects and ants;
3. birds: mainly feral pigeons and sparrows.

Surveys:

Regular surveys of food premises must be carried out to ensure that they are pest free. In particular, food storage rooms and dark, undisturbed areas should be examined. Signs to look for include:

1. live or dead bodies, including larvae and pupae;
2. droppings, or webbing from moths;
3. damage, including gnawing marks in food, wood or plaster, holes in sacks, boxes, packets or in the structure, chewed pieces of cardboard or paper;
4. spillages adjacent to sacks of food;
5. unusual smells – associated with mice and cockroaches in particular;
6. footprints and tail marks in dust or food powders such as flour;
7. rodent smears (black greasy marks) around pipes and holes and on walls adjacent to runways;
8. the loss of small amounts of food.

Regular surveys are essential

Reasons for control:

1. to prevent the spread of disease;

2   to prevent the wastage of food;

3   to prevent damage (fires and flooding caused by gnawing electric cables or pipes);

4   to prevent loss of custom (caused by selling contaminated food or because of the discomfort or fear of the public using public areas of a food premises which are infested with mice, cockroaches or wasps);

5   to avoid losing staff who will not wish to work in infested premises;

6   to comply with the law.

"Mice gnawed through your electrics? Look what they did to my hose!"

Food premises must be designed and constructed to minimize the risk of contamination from pests. External windows must, where necessary, be fitted with removable insect-proof screens. Adequate procedures must be in place to ensure pests are controlled. Refuse stores must be designed and managed to protect against access by pests. Food premises which are a health risk, for example, because of rodent infestation, are likely to be closed by local authority action.

General pest control:

Pests require food, shelter and security. Denial of these environmental factors will prevent their survival and is the first line of defence against possible infestations. Environmental control may be considered as denial of:

1   *access* – by care in design, maintenance and proofing of buildings. Doors and windows should be kept closed or if left open should be screened with a fine, cleansable mesh. Doorways can be protected with hanging plastic strips or air curtains and the bottom of wooden doors should be protected with metal plates. Access holes and other openings should be sealed with mortar, metal sheets or mesh;

2   *food and harbourage* – by good housekeeping.

Good housekeeping:

To reduce the risk of infestation it is important to prevent breeding and deny the lone invader the conditions it likes and in particular to ensure that:

1   premises and refuse areas are kept in a clean and tidy condition. Lids are always kept on waste bins which should be washed after emptying, together with the surrounding area. Waste must not be allowed to accumulate;

2   food on display or awaiting preparation is always kept covered;

3   spillages are cleared away promptly;

RODENTS

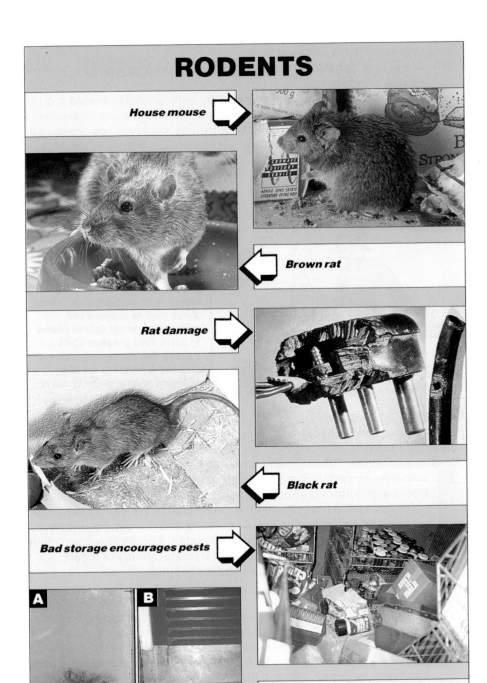

House mouse

Brown rat

Rat damage

Black rat

Bad storage encourages pests

(A) Rat smears
(B) Kick plate

COMMON FOOD PESTS

Wasp

Oriental cockroach

German cockroach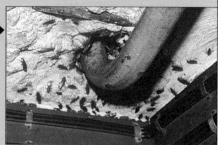

House flies

Fly eggs, maggots and pupae

Goods entrance

Proofing of doors and windows

COMMON FOOD PESTS

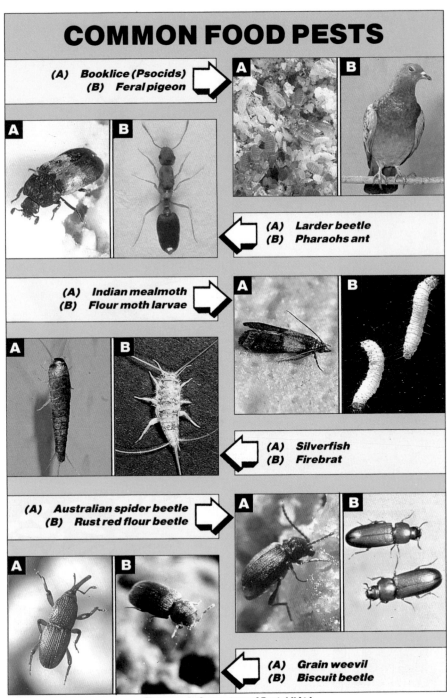

(A) Booklice (Psocids)
(B) Feral pigeon

(A) Larder beetle
(B) Pharaohs ant

(A) Indian mealmoth
(B) Flour moth larvae

(A) Silverfish
(B) Firebrat

(A) Australian spider beetle
(B) Rust red flour beetle

(A) Grain weevil
(B) Biscuit beetle

Photographs by courtesy of Rentokil Ltd.

4 food is stored off the floor and clear of walls to facilitate regular inspection. Stock should be checked regularly and damaged stock removed;

5 food is stored in rodent-proof containers and lids are always replaced;

6 all deliveries of raw materials, packaging and laundry are checked to ensure their freedom from infestation;

7 drains are kept clean and in good condition, a water trap is always maintained and gullies have tight-fitting metal grilles;

8 vegetation and other cover in the immediate vicinity of the food premises are removed;

9 sightings of pests or pest damage are reported to management immediately.

Physical and chemical control:

Although very important, environmental control may not be entirely successful and eradication must be achieved by using physical or chemical control methods.

Physical control methods are usually preferred as the pest is caught, either dead or alive, and consequently is not able to die in food, equipment or in some inaccessible place. Examples of physical control include ultra-violet, electric fly-killers, rodent traps and mist nets for birds. Sticky fly papers are unsightly but are useful in storage areas to alert you to flying insect problems.

Unfortunately physical methods are not always successful and poisons have to be used. Rodenticides are used to kill rats and mice, and insecticides to kill insects. Care must always be exercised when using poisons to ensure there is no risk of contaminating food. Food and small utensils must always be removed when using insecticide, especially sprays, and the premises and fixed equipment must be thoroughly cleaned after use. Infestations of food premises should be dealt with immediately and food handlers should seek assistance from the local authority or specialist contractor. The control of cockroaches or stored product insects is particularly difficult and requires an expert pest control operator.

What is a food pest?
Why must pests be kept out of food premises?
What are the signs of an infestation of food pests?
How can pests be controlled in food premises?
How can pests be kept out of food premises?

Cleaning and disinfection

Soiling of surfaces and equipment is unavoidable in all food businesses. It is essential that such residues are not allowed to accumulate to levels which expose food to risk of contamination. Removal of food residues, dirt and grease is the process of cleaning.

The reasons for cleaning

1 to remove matter on which bacteria would grow, thus reducing the risk of food poisoning and spoilage;

2 to allow disinfection* of specific equipment and surfaces;

3 to remove materials which would encourage pest infestations;

4 to reduce the risk of foreign matter contamination;

5 to ensure a pleasant and safe working environment;

6 to promote a favourable image to customers;

7 to comply with the law.

Energy in cleaning

Cleaning is the application of energy to a surface, with the intention of removing dirt and grease.

Energy is applied as:

physical, for example scrubbing;
heat, for example hot water;
chemical, for example detergent.**

Improving chemical energy and increasing heat will reduce the amount of physical energy required.

After cleaning, disinfectants*** are used to destroy bacteria that remain. Hot water, around 82°C, steam and bleach are the commonest disinfectants. Chemical disinfectants need time to work and an appropriate contact time is essential.

* *Disinfection – the reduction of micro-organisms to a level that is safe and which will not cause premature food spoilage.*

** *Detergent – a chemical used to remove grease, dirt and food particles.*

*** *Disinfectant – a chemical used for disinfection.*

Hot water, chemicals and physical energy must be used to clean

Effective cleaning

To be effective, cleaning must be planned. A schedule which stipulates the frequency, method of cleaning, the amount and type of chemical to use and the person responsible, must be drawn up and implemented.

Staff must be trained to **"clean as they go"** and they must always have regard to the provision of health and safety. Suitable protective clothing must be worn and the chemical manufacturer's instructions must always be followed. Some chemicals can be very dangerous if mixed. Open food must not be exposed to risk of contamination during cleaning.

Chemicals must always be stored separate from food and should never be emptied into unmarked or food containers, especially bottles.

After use the cleaning equipment itself must be cleaned and dried. Brushes and mops should be hung off the floor in non-food rooms or cupboards. Cleaning equipment used in toilets must not be used in food rooms.

Cleaning must be planned

Where to disinfect

Although food rooms and equipment need to be regularly and thoroughly cleaned, not everything requires disinfecting. Food contact surfaces and equipment, cutting boards, slicing machines, utensils, handles on drawers and refrigerators will need cleaning and disinfecting, often several times throughout the day and always following the use of raw food before high-risk food is prepared.

Walls, floors, drains and equipment legs require thorough cleaning and degreasing but are unlikely to require disinfection, unless there is a risk of food contamination. Ovens and similar devices which use high temperatures to destroy bacteria do not require disinfection.

The cleaning procedure

Cleaning and disinfection normally consists of six basic stages:

1 **pre-clean:** removing excess soil by sweeping, wiping or pre-rinsing;

2 **main clean:** loosening of the surface grease and dirt using a detergent;

3 **rinse:** removal of loose dirt and detergent;
4 **disinfection:** destroying micro-organisms using, for example bleach;
5 **final rinse:** removal of disinfectant;
6 **drying:** preferably natural by evaporating dry.

In light-soil conditions the pre-clean may be combined with the main clean. Soiled water must be changed as frequently as necessary. If air drying is not possible, single-use paper towels or a clean, dry cloth should be used.

Double-sink washing

Although the use of mechanical dishwashers and glasswashers is becoming more common, double-sink washing is recommended when suitable dishwashing machines are not available. The following procedure should be followed:

1 remove any heavy or loose soil by scraping and rinsing in cold water;
2 place articles in the first sink in detergent solution at 50°C to 60°C, scrub with a nylon brush and/or wipe with a clean cloth to loosen dirt residues. Rubber gloves will be required. Cool or dirty water should be replaced;
3 re-immerse in the first sink to wash off loosened dirt;
4 place articles in the second sink to rinse off chemical residues;
5 leave for 30 seconds at 82°C to achieve disinfection;
6 remove the articles, allow to drain and air dry on a clean, disinfected surface. After drying, store in a clean place free from contamination.

Why is it important to clean food premises and equipment regularly?
What is the difference between cleaning and disinfection?
What are the six basic stages in cleaning and disinfection?

Dishwashers are preferred

The walls, floors, doors, windows, ceiling, woodwork and all other parts of the structure of food rooms must be kept clean. Articles or equipment with which food comes into contact must be kept clean.

The law relating to food and food hygiene

The law is a complex subject and most acts and regulations affecting the food industry are difficult to comprehend. However, ignorance of the law is no defence in the event of a prosecution, and all food handlers should make special efforts to understand the legislation that affects their business and themselves. This book contains only very brief details of some of this legislation and more information may be obtained from the local environmental health officer.

Acts and regulations applicable to the food industry are concerned with:

1. the production or sale of injurious, unsafe, unfit or substandard food;
2. the contamination of food;
3. the hygiene of food premises, equipment and personnel;
4. hygiene practices, including temperature control and treatment;
5. the control of food poisoning and food-borne diseases;
6. the composition and labelling of food.

* Food Safety Act, 1990

This is the most important Act relating to the sale of food for human consumption. It contains comprehensive provisions for securing food safety and empowers Ministers to make extensive hygiene regulations. The provisions of the Act are applicable to all food businesses in England, Scotland and Wales.

* In Northern Ireland, the Food Safety (Northern Ireland) Order, 1991 applies.

It is an offence to render food injurious to health or to sell food which fails to comply with the food safety requirements by reason of it being injurious to health, unfit or so contaminated that it would be unreasonable to use it for human consumption.

An offence is also committed if food is sold which is not of the nature, substance or quality demanded by the purchaser. Legal action can be taken if food is falsely described or labelled.

Food which fails to comply with the food safety requirements or which is likely to cause food poisoning may be seized or detained by an authorised officer of a food authority. Expenses incurred in the destruction of food must be paid by the owner, although wrongful seizure can result in compensation.

A person found guilty of the above offences may be liable to a fine of up to £20,000 and/or imprisonment for up to six months, although in serious cases unlimited fines and up to two years imprisonment may be incurred.

Failure to comply with food hygiene regulations may result in the service of an **improvement notice** specifying the contraventions, the measures necessary to secure compliance and the time allowed for compliance. Failure to comply with the improvement notice is an offence.

When an authorised officer is satisfied that there is an imminent risk of injury to health he may issue an **emergency prohibition notice** which requires the closure of all or part of a food premises or the immediate prohibition of a process or use of equipment. An application must be made to the court for an **emergency prohibition order** within three days of serving the notice.

The court may also impose a prohibition on the proprietor or manager participating in the management of any food business.

It is a defence for a person to prove that he took **all reasonable precautions** and exercised **all due diligence** to avoid the commission of an offence by himself or by a person under his control.

Insanitary premises can be closed

Due diligence

Due diligence is the principal defence under the Food Safety Act, 1990 and enables a defendant to be acquitted of an offence if they prove that they "took all reasonable precautions and exercised all due diligence to avoid committing the offence". Taking reasonable precautions involves setting up a system of procedures and controls, having regard to the likely risks, and due diligence requires the systems to be operated properly. Written records will be essential and should include reference to specifications, training, testing, cleaning schedules and codes of practice.

Quality assurance and accreditation under British Standard 5750 will be beneficial but will not guarantee the success of a due diligence defence. A written warranty from a supplier will be useful but is no longer an absolute defence.

It may be acceptable for a food operator to prove that someone else, not under their control, was responsible, that they were relying on information provided, that reasonable checks were made, there was no reason to suspect they were committing an offence and they could not reasonably know that an offence was being committed.

The Food Safety (General Food Hygiene) Regulations, 1995

These Regulations control the hygiene standards of food premises other than those covered by their own specific regulations, such as dairies and slaughterhouses. The Regulations require:

1 Proprietors of food businesses to operate hygienically and to:
a) analyse food hazards that may arise in the food operation;
b) identify at which points in the operation these hazards may occur;
c) decide which of the points identified are critical to ensuring food safety (critical points);
d) implement effective control and monitoring procedures at these critical points and review these safety controls periodically and whenever food operations change.

2 Food premises must be kept clean and maintained in good repair and condition. They must be designed to permit good food hygiene practices, have adequate washbasins, flush lavatories and facilities for cleaning and disinfecting. Satisfactory standards of lighting and ventilation must be provided.

3 Walls, floors and food-contact surfaces of food rooms must be easy to clean and, where necessary, disinfect.

4 Conveyances and/or containers used for transporting foodstuffs must be kept clean and maintained in good repair and condition to protect foodstuffs from contamination.

5 Food equipment must be kept clean and in good repair and condition, to enable it to be kept clean and, where necessary, disinfected to minimize the risk of food contamination.

6 Food waste and refuse must not be allowed to accumulate in food rooms and adequate provision must be made for its storage and removal.

7 An adequate supply of potable (drinking) water must be provided.

8 Food handlers must keep themselves clean and wear suitable clean and where appropriate protective clothing. If they know or suspect they are carrying a food-borne disease, or have an infected wound or skin condition, they must advise their manager and must not be permitted to work if they are likely to contaminate food with pathogens.

9 Food, including raw materials, must be fit for human consumption and stored and protected to minimize any risk of contamination.

10 Food handlers must be supervised and instructed and/or trained in food hygiene matters commensurate with their work activities.

11 Offences are punishable, on conviction, by a fine of up to £5,000 for each offence. In serious cases a sentence of up to two years imprisonment and unlimited fines may be imposed

*Food must not be exposed to
risk of contamination*

Food Safety (Temperature Control) Regulations, 1995

Food which needs to be kept chilled because it is likely to support the growth of pathogens or the formation of toxins must be kept at or below 8°C. Certain foods, for example, raw food intended for cooking, are exempt, however, no food must be kept at a temperature which would result in a risk to health. (This may mean that some foods have to be stored below 8°C). Limited periods outside temperature control, consistent with food safety, are permitted for preparation, transport, display and service.

Cooked food which needs to be kept hot to control the growth of pathogens or the formation of toxins must be kept at or above 63°C. Certain exemptions exist, for example, food displayed for less than 2 hours. Where food has to be cooled it must be done as quickly as possible.

The Food Premises (Registration) Regulations, 1991

These Regulations require food premises to register with their local authority. Small bed and breakfast establishments, slaughterhouses and certain premises controlled by charitable organisations are included in the exemptions. A fine of up to £1,000 for failure to register or £5,000 for providing false information are the penalties for non-compliance.

The law relating to health and safety

The Health and Safety at Work etc. Act, 1974

This is the principal Act concerned with protecting the health and safety of employees and members of the public.

Every employer has a legal obligation to ensure, as far as is reasonably practicable, the health, safety and welfare of employees. Safe systems of work must be devised and supervision and training given to all staff, for example before staff are allowed to operate or clean dangerous machines, such as gravity feed slicers.

Employees must ensure that their acts or omissions do not adversely affect other persons.

The Control of Substances Hazardous to Health Regulations, 1988

These Regulations provide a legal framework for the control of substances hazardous to health. They apply to all types of business including food businesses. The essential measures that employers (and sometimes employees) have to take to ensure people are protected from the hazardous substances they may encounter are stipulated. Hazardous substances include those that are toxic, harmful, irritant or corrosive, for example cleaning chemicals and pesticides.

Environmental health officers

Environmental health officers are empowered to enter, inspect and close insanitary food premises. They will identify unsafe practices, investigate food complaints and incidents of food-borne disease. **Improvement and prohibition notices** may be issued, food seized or detained and legal proceedings instituted for contraventions of legislation.

However, they are employed to protect the public and usually prefer to give advice and offer guidance, especially at the planning stage. Don't hesitate to contact them if you need assistance.

> **What are the important pieces of legislation relating to food safety and hygiene?**
> **What action can be taken by a local authority to control the sale of unsafe, unfit, contaminated or substandard food?**
> **What action can be taken if food premises are unhygienic or substandard?**
> **What are the requirements of current legislation regarding, premises, equipment, food handlers, washing facilities, services, practices and storage temperatures?**
> **When can insanitary food premises be closed?**

General rules for food handlers

1 Food handlers with skin, nose, throat or bowel trouble must inform their supervisor and must not handle food until medical clearance has been obtained.

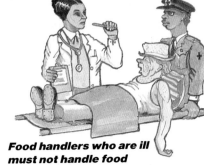

Food handlers who are ill must not handle food

2 Cuts, burns and sores must be covered with waterproof dressings. Persons with boils or septic cuts must not handle food. Fingernails must be kept clean and short, and nail varnish should not be used.

3 Suitable protective clothing and head covering must be worn by all food handlers. Outdoor clothing must not be brought into food rooms. Jewellery, hair grips and watches should be removed.

Food handlers should look

LIKE THIS

NOT LIKE THIS

4 Food handlers must not smoke in food rooms or whilst handling open food.

5 On entering a food room all food handlers should wash their hands. Hands must also be thoroughly washed after visiting the w.c., handling raw food, blowing the nose, handling refuse or swill, eating, smoking, cleaning and at frequent intervals during the work period.

Avoid sneezing over food

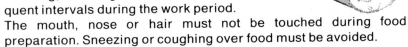

6 The mouth, nose or hair must not be touched during food preparation. Sneezing or coughing over food must be avoided.

7 All equipment, fixtures and fittings must be clean before preparation begins.

8	Raw food must always be kept separate from high-risk food at all stages of storage and preparation. Separate equipment, working surfaces and food handlers should be used to avoid cross-contamination from raw to high-risk food.
9	Frozen meat must be completely thawed before cooking. Thawing must be carried out separately from other processes. The liquid from defrosting poultry, etc. must not come into contact with other food, directly or indirectly, for example by use of a wiping cloth.
10	All meat must be cooked thoroughly. Rewarming cooked meats is potentially hazardous. All reheated foods including meat, soup and gravy must be thoroughly reheated and consumed immediately.
11	If hot meat is not to be eaten immediately, it must be cooled quickly and placed in a refrigerator within $1\frac{1}{2}$ hours. Cooked food must be protected from contamination at all times and kept out of the **danger zone of temperature,** i.e. 5°C to 63°C.
12	Food must not be removed from the refrigerator until required for serving or preparation.
13	Display trolleys and buffets should be refrigerated and covered to prevent contamination.
14	Stored food must be rotated to prevent spoilage, avoid waste and prevent infestations. Out-of-date food and damaged canned or packaged food must not be sold.
15	Dirty pans, cutlery, crockery and other equipment should be cleaned and disinfected without undue delay.
16	If the use of drying cloths is unavoidable, they must be kept clean.
17	Dirty wiping cloths must not be used. Disposable cloths are preferred.
18	Spillages should be cleaned up promptly and food debris should not be allowed to accumulate.
19	Polythene sacks or suitable impervious containers, fitted with lids, should be used for the disposal of waste in food rooms.
20	Animals must not be allowed in food rooms. Infestations of insects or rodents must be reported immediately.

Dirty food handlers will be prosecuted

**REMEMBER,
YOUR CARELESSNESS
MIGHT BE THE CAUSE
OF AN OUTBREAK OF
FOOD POISONING**

The identification of steps critical to food safety (hazard analysis and control)

The Food Safety (General Food Hygiene) Regulations, 1995 require proprietors of food businesses to identify any step in the activities of the food business which is critical to ensuring food safety and ensure that appropriate safety measures are implemented to avoid risk to health.

Large food manufacturers with relatively few product lines may comply with this requirement by using a fully documented Hazard Analysis Critical Control Point (HACCP) System. An alternative approach to identifying and controlling steps critical to food safety will be more appropriate for other food businesses, especially catering and retailing, which have a large number of products often prepared simultaneously with a degree of flexibility inapplicable to manufacturing.

However, improvements in consistency and adherence to laid down procedures by catering and retailing businesses make the application of risk assessment and the implementation of controls much more effective and enhance product safety.

To comply with the legislation, proprietors will need to examine their operation from purchase of raw materials to service of the customer on the basis of the following five principles:

1   *Analysis of the food hazards associated with the food business operation.*

A hazard is anything that may cause harm to the consumer. The three main hazards in relation to food are:

(i) Bacteria or other microorganisms, and their toxins, that cause food poisoning.

(ii) Chemical contamination, for example, cleaning chemicals.

(iii) Foreign bodies such as glass or metal.

2   *Identification of the points in the operation where food hazards may occur.*

Food will pass through many steps, including purchase, receipt, storage, preparation, cooking, cooling, display and service, until final consumption by the customer. Hazards can occur at any of these steps and should be identified, preferably on a flow diagram, for each type of food or group of foods.

The particular hazards to consider at each step are:

(i) The presence of the contaminant in the raw food or ingredient, for example, salmonella in raw chicken.

(ii) If the food can become contaminated at a particular step, for example, storage of raw food and high-risk food together.

(iii) If bacteria can multiply or produce toxin, for example, because food is left at room temperature for too long.

(iv) If microorganisms are able to survive a particular process, such as cooking or disinfection, which should have killed them.

3 *Deciding which of the points identified are critical to ensuring food safety ("critical points").*

At each step there are likely to be several hazards and the points at which the hazards must be controlled to ensure food safety should be considered as critical control points. Bacterial contamination may occur during preparation of high-risk food, for example, from unhygienic utensils or working surface, the hands of staff or raw food. Bacterial growth may occur if food is held at room temperature for too long.

4 *Identification and implementation of effective control and monitoring procedures at the critical points.*

Controls must be implemented to eliminate the hazard or reduce it to a safe level. Measurable targets should be set and checks introduced to ensure targets are achieved. Temperature and times are two of the most important parameters as they are precise and relatively easy to monitor. For example, high-risk foods should be stored at or below 5°C and should not be left at ambient temperature for longer than 15 minutes. Personal hygiene controls are not as precise, although effective supervision should ensure instructions are adhered to, for example, staff must wash their hands when entering the food room, after handling raw meat and at specific times during the day. Bacteriological cleanliness of equipment will require cleaning and disinfection of equipment at specific times in accordance with cleaning schedules.

Records are necessary for managers to ensure that the necessary monitoring has been undertaken. Written procedures on corrective action in event of targets not being met are also essential.

5 *Review of the analysis of food hazards, critical control points and the control and monitoring procedures periodically, and whenever the food business operations change.*

A review of the hazard analysis and control system will be necessary if:

(i) Controls are ineffective or the product is unsatisfactory.

(ii) The range or type of product alters, for example, cooked chicken is purchased instead of raw.

(iii) The method of preparation changes, for example, a microwave oven replaces conventional cooking.

(iv) New equipment is introduced, for example, a new refrigerator, blast chiller or oven.

Documentation of the system is not a legal requirement but effective documentation, which is implemented, will impress enforcement officers and commercial customers and assist a defence of due diligence in the event of prosecution. It is also extremely difficult to consistently apply controls and checks if there is no documentation.

EXAMPLES OF HAZARDS, CONTROLS AND MONITORING AT STEPS IN THE OPERATION CRITICAL TO FOOD SAFETY

STEP	HAZARD	CONTROL	MONITORING
Purchase of raw materials	Presence of contaminants, especially pathogens or toxins (inherent contaminants).	Select least hazardous ingredients. Only use reputable suppliers (approved suppliers list). Specification for product quality and safety including delivery temperatures.	Inspect supplier or request records to show that they follow good manufacturing practice. Historical check of deliveries. Absence of customer complaints. Bacteriological sampling.
Receipt of raw materials	Contamination of food, especially by pathogens/toxins. Multiplication of food poisoning bacteria.	Specify delivery requirements, especially time and temperature. Minimize time for unloading/placing in storage. Deboxing area. Staff training.	Check delivery vehicles and drivers, date codes, time for unloading and temperature and condition of food (as per specification). Competency testing of staff.
Storage (chilled, frozen and dry)	Multiplication of food poisoning bacteria. Contamination due to poor hygiene practices.	Store at correct temperature (alarmed units). Cover/wrap food. Stock rotation/date codes. Separate raw/high-risk foods. Cleaning/disinfection. Good housekeeping. Pest control/pest proof containers. Staff training.	Check air/food temperatures, date codes, pest control and food complaint records. Audits and visual checks of food. Cleaning schedules. Competency testing of staff.
Preparation	Multiplication of food poisoning bacteria. Contamination due to poor hygiene practices.	Prepare minimum amount of food. Minimize time at room temperature. Good personal hygiene/training. Separate raw/high-risk foods. Colour coding. Cleaning/disinfection. Good hygiene practices, organization/workflow.	Check time/temperature. Audits/visual checks. Competency testing of staff. Cleaning schedules. Bacteriological swabbing of surfaces. Equipment maintenance. Design. Electronic fly killers.
Cooking	Survival of pathogens/toxins. Contamination and multiplication.	Centre temperature at least 75°C. Ensure frozen poultry/joints completely thawed. Staff training.	Check time/temperature. Equipment maintenance. Audits. Competency testing of staff.
Cooling	Multiplication of surviving food poisoning bacteria or germination of spores. Toxin production. Contamination.	Weight/thickness of joints. Cool rapidly (blast chiller). Keep covered. No contact with raw food. Good personal hygiene/training. Cleaning/disinfection.	Check time/temperature. Audits/visual checks. Equipment maintenance. Competency testing of staff. Cleaning schedules.
Service	Multiplication of food poisoning bacteria. Contamination.	Keep <5°C or >63°C. Good personal hygiene/training. Keep covered. Cleaning/disinfection. Sell within shelf-life. Prevent customer contamination.	Check time/temperature. Audits/visual checks. Competency testing of staff. Cleaning schedules. Equipment maintenance.

Safety in the kitchen

It is essential that all persons engaged in the preparation, cooking and service of food are aware at all times of the need for certain elementary precautions of safety, in order to automatically minimize the risk of accident.

1	Do not leave metal spoons in boiling liquids.
2	Do not leave handles of cooking pans over the gas flame.
3	Always carry a knife with its point towards the floor.
4	Never attempt to catch a falling knife.
5	Always cut or chop on a board. Never in the hand.
6	When using a hand model can-opener, protect the other hand with a cloth or kitchen towel.
7	Always clean up any spilled water, grease or fat from the floor immediately.
8	Never use a damp cloth for lifting or carrying hot utensils.
9	Never wear sandals or open shoes in the kitchen.
10	Pans containing hot fat which catch fire should be extinguished by smothering with a fire blanket or a thick damp sack. Never pour water on a fat or oil fire.
11	Long hair styles should be 'put up' and covered with a clean head cap or similar means of protection.
12	For economy, as well as safety, all gas and electrical appliances must be turned **off** when not in use.
13	Make sure that the **first aid** box is readily accessible and that it contains sufficient waterproof dressings and burn dressings.
14	Never attempt to carry large, heavy containers of hot food single-handed. Get assistance.
15	Do not reach over naked burning appliances.
16	Always ensure that gravity meat slicers are adequately guarded.
17	Ensure that all drainage channel covers are properly fitted.
18	Never put cleaning fluids into bottles originally used for food or drink, e.g. lemonade or milk bottles.
19	Do not obstruct fire exits, stairways or corridors.
20	Ensure stacked goods and boxes are safe.
21	Keep chemicals in a locked cupboard away from food.
22	Keep drawers shut and ensure knife blades are always face down.
23	Report dangerous equipment, especially faulty electrical plugs/wiring and trailing leads.
24	Follow the advice on safety signs.
NB	Health and Safety training of staff is essential and in most circumstances a legal requirement.

By courtesy of the City of Canterbury Environmental Health Department.

Glossary

Additive	A chemical added to food, for example, a preservative, a colouring or flavouring agent.
Aerobic	Using oxygen.
Anaerobic	Using little or no oxygen.
Antibiotic	A drug used to destroy pathogenic bacteria within human or animal bodies.
Antiseptic	A substance that prevents the growth of bacteria and moulds, specifically on or in the human body.
Bactericide	A substance which destroys bacteria.
Binary fission	A type of reproduction where the organism divides into two.
Carrier	A person who harbours, and may transmit, pathogenic organisms without showing signs of illness.
Cleaning	The removal of soil, food residues, dirt, grease and other objectionable matter.
Coliforms	Bacteria whose presence can indicate poor hygiene.
Contamination	The occurrence of any objectionable matter in food.
Cook-chill	A type of food production system where food is prepared, cooked, rapidly, cooled and kept, for a limited time period, under chilled storage prior to reheating.
Danger zone of bacterial growth	The temperature range within which multiplication of pathogenic bacteria is possible (from 5°C to 63°C).
Dehydrate	To remove water.
Detergent	A chemical used to remove grease, dirt and food particles.
Disinfectant	A chemical used to reduce the number of micro-organisms to a level that is safe and which will not cause premature food spoilage.
E.C. Directive	Legislation from the European Community that has to be included into member country laws.
Enzyme	A type of protein that speeds up a biological process and is unchanged by it.
First-aid materials	Suitable and sufficient bandages and dressings, including waterproof dressings. All dressings to be individually wrapped.
Food business	Any business in the course of which commercial operations with respect to food or food sources are carried out (whether carried on for profit or not).
Food-borne illness	An illness resulting from the consumption of food contaminated by pathogenic micro-organisms (and/or toxins) which do not usually multiply within the food.
Food hygiene	All measures necessary to ensure the safety and wholesomeness of food during preparation, processing, manufacture, storage, transportation, distribution, handling and offering for sale or supply to the consumer.